C000051825

PEANUTS
GUIDE TO LIFE
Book 2

By Charles M. Schulz

RAVETTE PUBLISHING

This edition published by Ravette Publishing 2007.

ISBN 978-1-84161-269-0

CONTENTS

Peanuts Guide to:

Life's Little
Quirks

"A HOT DOG JUST DOESN'T TASTE RIGHT WITHOUT A BALL GAME IN FRONT OF IT!"

Charlie Brown

"THAT'S LIFE . . . PEOPLE GO AWAY,
AND DOGS STAY HOME . . ."

Charlie Brown

"I GUESS BABYSITTERS ARE LIKE
USED CARS. . . YOU NEVER REALLY KNOW
WHAT YOU'RE GETTING. . ."

Schroeder

"A WATCHED SUPPER DISH NEVER FILLS!"

Snoopy

"THERE'S NOTHING THAT CAN HARM
A PERSON MORE THAN TOO MUCH
FORMAL EDUCATION!"

Linus

"IT'S IMPOSSIBLE TO BE
GLOOMY WHEN YOU'RE SITTING BEHIND
A MARSHMALLOW . . ."

Lucy

"IN THE BOOK OF LIFE,
THE ANSWERS ARE NOT IN THE BACK!"

Charlie Brown

Love

"IT'S AMAZING HOW STUPID
YOU CAN BE WHEN YOU'RE IN LOVE..."

Lucy

"WHEN NO ONE LOVES YOU, YOU HAVE TO PRETEND THAT EVERYONE LOVES YOU!"

Sally

"LOVE IS NOT KNOWING WHAT
YOU'RE TALKING ABOUT."

Lucy

"LOVE MAKES YOU DO STRANGE THINGS. . ."

Charlie Brown

People Skills

"IF YOU CAN'T BEAT 'EM,
COOPERATE 'EM TO DEATH!"

Charlie Brown

"IN FIRST-AID CLASS I LEARNED
THAT IF YOU HAVE OFFENDED SOMEONE,
THE BEST TREATMENT IS TO APOLOGIZE
IMMEDIATELY. . ."

Marcie

"THE AVERAGE DAD NEEDS LOTS OF ENCOURAGEMENT."

Charlie Brown

"WHEN YOU GET A COMPLIMENT,
ALL YOU HAVE TO SAY IS 'THANK YOU'."

Classmate talking to Rerun

Other PEANUTS Gift Books available ...

	ISBN	Price
A Friend is ... forever	978-1-84161-213-3	£4.99
Best Friends ... understand sharing	978-1-84161-258-4	£4.99
Happiness is ... a warm puppy	978-1-84161-211-9	£4.99
Love is ... walking hand in hand	978-1-84161-212-6	£4.99
Peanuts Guide to Life Book 1	978-1-84161-268-3	£4.99
Peanuts Guide to Life Book 3	978-1-84161-287-4	£4.99
Security is ... a thumb and a blanket	978-1-84161-210-2	£4.99
True Love is ... complete trust	978-1-84161-259-1	£4.99

HOW TO ORDER   Please send a cheque/postal order in £ sterling, made payable to 'Ravette Publishing' for the cover price of the books and allow the following for post & packaging ...

UK & BFPO   70p for the first book & 40p per book thereafter
Europe & Eire   £1.30 for the first book & 70p per book thereafter
Rest of the world   £2.20 for the first book & £1.10 per book thereafter

RAVETTE PUBLISHING LTD
Unit 3 Tristar Centre, Star Road, Partridge Green, West Sussex RH13 8RA
Tel: 01403 711443   Fax: 01403 711554   Email: ravettepub@aol.com

Prices and availability are subject to change without prior notice.